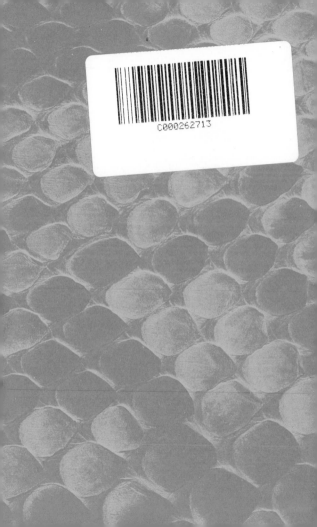

KILLER OZ

Great white shark
Carcharodon carcharias

KILLER OZ

**A collection of the
50 most deadly and dangerous
Australian animals and plants.**

INTRODUCTION

Australians love to tease overseas visitors with tall tales of the mortal dangers that lurk everywhere from the dunny, the backyard pool and the bush, to the outback and the beautiful blue waters off our inviting white sand beaches.

It's true that we boast some of the world's most venomous snakes and lethal spiders, and that our tropical waters are home to toxic jellyfish and killer crocodiles – all this deadly animal action could be viewed as evidence for how wild and remote Australia is. Conflict between people and animals in more urbanised and populated parts of the world has long since vanquished species that might have threatened human progress.

In this book we present 50 of our most dangerous organisms, both animals and plants. Some are lethal, others are less so, but can still inflict pain and injury. A few are aggressive and most strike in self-defence, albeit very rarely – the truth is that you are at far greater risk when you get behind the wheel of your car.

Treat all wildlife with respect. Observe warning signs and basic common sense when you enter their territory, and enjoy this line-up of some of our most amazing (and dangerous) flora and fauna.

Lowlands copperhead
Austrelaps superbus

CONTENTS

Eastern mouse spider
Missulena sp.

DID YOU KNOW?
Juvenile eastern brown snakes are born with black heads and copper-coloured bodies.

EASTERN BROWN SNAKE
Pseudonaja textilis

ALSO KNOWN AS: COMMON BROWN SNAKE

Brown snakes, including fast-moving and aggressive eastern brown snakes, kill more people every year in Australia than any other group. Not only is their venom ranked the second most toxic of any land snake in the world, they thrive on farms with plenty of mice and in populated areas.

HOW AND WHERE IT WILL STRIKE
If disturbed, it winds its raised body into an 'S' shape, mouth gaping and ready to strike. Its venom causes progressive paralysis and prevents blood clotting, which may take many antivenom doses to reverse. Victims can collapse within just a few minutes.

DISTRIBUTION
Eastern half of mainland Australia.

11
Estimated number of deaths from this snake since the 1990s.

COASTAL TAIPAN
Oxyuranus scutellatus

ALSO KNOWN AS: EASTERN TAIPAN

These slim brown snakes are extremely deadly. Before the 1956 introduction of a specialised antivenom, taipan bites were almost always fatal and caused many human deaths. The venom affects the nervous system and blood, causing nausea, convulsions, internal bleeding and muscle and kidney damage. Death can occur in just 30 minutes.

HOW AND WHERE IT WILL STRIKE
Nervous and alert, they're not usually confrontational and would rather escape any threat. But they'll put up a ferocious defence when surprised or cornered, 'freezing' before hurling their body forward to inflict several lightning-fast snapping bites.

DISTRIBUTION
Along the east coast from northern NSW to Brisbane, and in northern WA. They are fond of sugarcane fields.

?

Deaths from this snake have occurred, but the total number is unverified.

DID YOU KNOW?
Coastal taipans are
equipped with the longest
fangs of any Australian
snake (13mm), and have
the third most toxic
venom of any land snakes.

DID YOU KNOW?
Female death
adders give birth
to live young in
litters of 10–33
snakelets.

COMMON DEATH ADDER

Acanthophis antarcticus

ALSO KNOWN AS: SOUTHERN DEATH ADDER

This ambush predator waits motionless, concealed in leaf litter, sand or gravel, twitching the worm-like lure on the end of its tail to attract prey. More than half of death adder bites proved fatal before the introduction of antivenom. The venom contains a type of neurotoxin that causes loss of motor and sensory functions, including respiration, resulting in paralysis and death.

DISTRIBUTION
Eastern Australia (except the far north and south), and southern SA and WA.

HOW AND WHERE IT WILL STRIKE
Unlike other snakes that flee approaching humans, common death adders are more likely to sit tight and risk being stepped on, making them dangerous to unwary bushwalkers. They are reluctant to bite unless touched.

60%
of bites were fatal before the introduction of antivenom.

DUGITE
Pseudonaja affinis

ALSO KNOWN AS: SPOTTED BROWN SNAKE

These snakes have shiny brown scales with small dark spots. Found around houses, golf clubs and parks, dugites like to hide under anything at all, from sheets of tin to rocks or tree stumps. They are extremely dangerous to humans, as they like to live around houses, hunting mice, and can fit easily through tiny holes.

HOW AND WHERE IT WILL STRIKE
This snake is easily frightened and will shape its body into an 'S' before striking with lightning speed and biting with small but very sharp fangs. It will aim high on the limbs, meaning it often bites above the tops of boots that its fangs could not penetrate.

DISTRIBUTION
Southern WA and south-eastern SA.

70%
of snake bites presented at Perth hospital are from this snake.

1
Recorded death.

LAND

DID YOU KNOW?
The mulga snake can happily munch on other snakes, including venomous ones. It is however extremely susceptible to poison from the introduced cane toad.

MULGA SNAKE
Pseudechis australis

ALSO KNOWN AS: KING BROWN SNAKE

This is Australia's heaviest venomous snake. It also has the largest recorded venom output of any in Australia – 1350mg in one bite (the maximum tiger snake yield is less than 230mg). Although commonly known as king browns, mulgas belong to the black snake genus *Pseudechis*, and black snake antivenom is needed to treat their bites.

HOW AND WHERE IT WILL STRIKE

Temperaments seems to vary with location. Southern mulgas are reportedly shy and quiet, but agitated northern snakes throw their heads from side to side and hiss loudly. Mulgas bite savagely, even hanging on and chewing as they inject massive amounts of venom that destroys blood cells.

DISTRIBUTION
Throughout Australia, except Victoria, Tasmania and the most southerly parts of WA.

!

Certainly venomous, but deaths from mulga snakes are rare.

RED-BELLIED BLACK SNAKE
Pseudechis porphyriacus

ALSO KNOWN AS: COMMON BLACK SNAKE

The red-bellied black is somewhat less venomous than many other Australian snakes, but you're more likely to come across it in urban areas and it's also one of the few large venomous snakes still found around Sydney. Its bite can cause significant illness that requires medical attention. It can grow up to 2m long and will eat other snakes.

DISTRIBUTION
East coast (though not in Tasmania) and slightly into south-eastern SA.

0

No deaths have been confirmed from bites by this species.

HOW AND WHERE IT WILL STRIKE
Red-bellied blacks are not usually aggressive and prefer to avoid humans if possible. But when threatened they'll flatten their bodies and hiss loudly. The venom affects blood-clotting and causes muscle and nerve damage.

DID YOU KNOW?
Pregnant red-bellied black females are known to congregate in groups basking in the sun.

23

DID YOU KNOW?
Collett's snake venom is like that of the mulga (p18) in terms of its potency and effect on humans, causing muscle and kidney damage and bleeding.

COLLETT'S SNAKE
Pseudechis colletti

ALSO KNOWN AS: DOWN'S TIGER SNAKE,
COLLETT'S BLACK SNAKE

This distinctively patterned reptile is commonly regarded as one of Australia's most spectacularly marked snakes. It has pink to bright red bands or blotches against a grey to reddish brown ground colour. They are found in cracking clay soils in outback Queensland where they shelter within deep cracks.

DISTRIBUTION
Outback Queensland.

HOW AND WHERE IT WILL STRIKE
Collett's snakes are extremely secretive and rarely seen. They have long been popular with reptile keepers, so any bites are likely to occur through handling.

0

No recorded fatalities, but a few bites have been documented; there is little doubt this snake is potentially deadly.

HIGHLANDS COPPERHEAD
Austrelaps ramsayi

ALSO KNOWN AS: ALPINE COPPERHEAD

This snake has distinctive, prominently barred upper lips and is extremely venomous. It can be found slithering around swamps and marshes hunting frogs, lizards, small birds and mammals and sometimes other snakes.

HOW AND WHERE IT WILL STRIKE

Like most snakes, the highlands copperhead is not aggressive, but will attack if threatened. It will flatten its body to appear larger and thrash its tail while hissing loudly to scare away predators. If this doesn't work, the copperhead will bite, delivering a nasty venom that can potentially kill without the proper medical attention.

DISTRIBUTION
Highlands of New South Wales and Victoria.

0
No deaths have been recorded.

DID YOU KNOW?
Copperheads are among
the few snakes that give
birth to live young.

DID YOU KNOW?
Western browns extend
throughout the vast
sandy desert regions.

WESTERN BROWN SNAKE
Pseudonaja mengdeni

ALSO KNOWN AS: GWARDAR,
COLLARED BROWN SNAKE

Said to be less aggressive than its eastern cousin, the western brown snake is still highly dangerous and part of the group of snakes that cause most fatalities in Australia. Western browns tend to be fast-moving and nervous in temperament.

HOW AND WHERE IT WILL STRIKE

When disturbed, they will run for cover, striking quickly if cornered before making a quick getaway. Bites are usually painless and difficult to see due to the small fang marks. Victims will experience headache, nausea, abdominal pain, severe coagulopathy (impaired blood clotting) and sometimes kidney damage.

DISTRIBUTION

Most of mainland Australia, but absent from the wetter fringes of eastern Australia and south-western WA.

?

There are thought to have been some deaths but the exact number is unknown.

INLAND TAIPAN
Oxyuranus microlepidotus

ALSO KNOWN AS: FIERCE SNAKE,
SMALL-SCALED SNAKE

Because this reclusive snake lives in remote, open habitat in inland Australia, it rarely encounters people. That's fortunate because it's on the world's top 10 deadliest snakes list. Its venom is considered the most potent of any land snake anywhere; with the potential to kill an adult human. It hunts in the burrows of long-haired rats where it needs to finish off prey quickly to avoid injury, which may explain why its venom needs to be so potent.

HOW AND WHERE IT WILL STRIKE
You're unlikely to encounter one unless you're a desert dweller. But if you do, and it bites, seek medical attention immediately.

DISTRIBUTION
Central Australia, but may extend further than presently known.

0
No deaths recorded and all recorded bites to date have been inflicted upon snake handlers.

DID YOU KNOW?
Effective first aid can mean the difference between life and death for anyone bitten by a venomous Australian snake. Immobilisation and the correct application of a pressure bandage can help buy time while you await medical assistance.

DID YOU KNOW?
This snake lives in cold climates and can become irritable when it gets too hot.

LOWLANDS COPPERHEAD

Austrelaps superbus

Water lovers, lowlands copperheads are at home around dams, soaks, canals and along the verges of roads. They feed on frogs, lizards and smaller snakes and occasionally shelter in other creature's burrows. Their fangs are short, so thick socks or shoes are able to provide some protection.

HOW AND WHERE IT WILL STRIKE

Copperheads are shy and prefer to avoid humans, although they live in populated and agricultural areas. If cornered, they will hiss loudly, flatten their body and flick or thrash about, usually without biting. With further provocation they may lash out, although they are slow to strike and can be inaccurate.

DISTRIBUTION

South-eastern Australia, southern Victoria, Tasmania and the islands of Bass Strait.

!

Copperhead venom affects the nervous system, ruptures blood cells and damages muscles – but it is rarely fatal.

TIGER SNAKE
Notechis scutatus

ALSO KNOWN AS: COMMON TIGER SNAKE

This snake is responsible for the second-highest number of bites in Australia because it's found in highly populated areas along the east coast, including some metropolitan areas of Melbourne. Tiger snakes are attracted to farms and outer suburbs, where they hunt mice. They can easily be trodden on by unsuspecting victims.

HOW AND WHERE IT WILL STRIKE

It flattens its neck and strikes low when threatened. They cause pain in the feet and neck, tingling, numbness and sweating, then breathing difficulties and paralysis. The venom damages blood and muscles and can be fatal if left untreated.

DISTRIBUTION

Across southern Australia including Tasmania, with isolated populations as far north as southern Queensland.

8

Estimated number of deaths from tiger snake bites since the late 1800s.

LAND

DID YOU KNOW?
The small-eyed snake has a pink or red stomach, but unlike the red-bellied black snake you can't see it until the snake rolls over, but it's best to leave this snake alone and take our word for it.

SMALL-EYED SNAKE
Cryptophis nigrescens

ALSO KNOWN AS: EASTERN SMALL-EYED SNAKE

At about 50cm long, the small-eyed snake may be petite but its venom can pack a punch. Although common, these snakes are secretive and nocturnal and so don't often come into contact with humans. Coloured black or dark grey with a pink belly, they blend into the night. When disturbed they may thrash about aggressively, but are not usually inclined to bite.

HOW AND WHERE IT WILL STRIKE
The venom's toxicity is poorly known, but bites have caused illness in snake handlers and at least one fatality. It contains a long-acting toxin that can attack muscle tissue (including in the heart) for days after a bite.

DISTRIBUTION
Along the east coast, from Victoria to the Cape York peninsula.

1
Number of recorded deaths.

Tiger snake
Notechis scutatus

SYDNEY FUNNEL-WEB SPIDER
Atrax robustus

The Sydney funnel-web is recognised as one of the world's most deadly spiders. The immediate effects of a bite are severe pain at the site, followed by profuse sweating and saliva production and muscle tremors, with pain and cramps spreading to other parts of the body. Rapid first aid is essential and antivenom must be administered as soon as possible. There have been no deaths since the antivenom was released in 1981.

HOW AND WHERE IT WILL STRIKE
The greatest risk comes from adult males, which wander about at night looking for mates during the warmest months – from November to April.

DISTRIBUTION
In forested areas around Sydney, but there are about 40 other funnel-web species along the east coast.

13

Number of fatalities attributed to the Sydney funnel-web between 1927 and the release of an antivenom in 1981.

DID YOU KNOW?
In a bizarre twist of evolution, humans and other primates are affected by funnel-web venom but native Australian mammals are not.

DID YOU KNOW?
Cupboard spiders (*Steatoda* sp.) are often mistaken for redbacks, and their venom, though less potent, produces similar symptoms. Redback antivenom is effective against their bites as well.

REDBACK SPIDER
Latrodectus hasselti

Redback spiders are found throughout Australia, in diverse habitats, including urban areas. They often hide in dry, sheltered places such as garden sheds, mailboxes and under toilet seats. About 2000 bites are reported each year, about 250 of which will need antivenom. No deaths have been recorded since redback antivenom became available in the 1950s.

DISTRIBUTION
Australia-wide.

0

No confirmed deaths since the 1950s.

HOW AND WHERE IT WILL STRIKE
The venom can be dangerous, but the small redback fangs make many bites ineffective. The main symptom of envenomation is severe and persistent pain, which can last hours to days. There may also be nausea, malaise and lethargy.

WOLF SPIDER
Family: Lycosidae

These stout-bodied, grey-to-brown, ground-dwelling spiders vary in body size from about 1cm to 8cm. The front half – the carapace – is raised and often has markings radiating from the centre, which has led to the alternate name 'Union Jack' spiders. Wolf spiders are efficient hunters and use their large eyes on night hunts to find and run down their prey, which are mainly insects.

HOW AND WHERE IT WILL STRIKE
Wolf spiders are not especially aggressive and usually hide in their burrows by day. The danger is when you're working in the garden – you may dig one up and accidentally provoke a bite, which can be very painful.

DISTRIBUTION:
Australia-wide.

0
No recorded deaths from this species. Although wolf spiders are venomous, their bites are not lethal but may cause rapid pulse, dizziness and nausea.

DID YOU KNOW?
Their name is derived
from the belief that
they hunted in packs
like wolves.

DID YOU KNOW?
Tarantulas form a hammock
out of silk in which they lie
when they moult, as this
process can take several
hours for a large spider.

AUSTRALIAN TARANTULA
Family: Theraphosidae

ALSO KNOWN AS: BIRD-EATING SPIDER, WHISTLING SPIDER, BARKING SPIDER

Australia's native tarantulas are also known as whistling or barking spiders because of the sounds most species produce by rubbing rows of modified spines against the bases of their jaws. These spiders mostly feed on insects, other spiders, lizards and frogs and occasionally bird hatchlings. Only seven species have been officially identified, but it's likely many more exist.

HOW AND WHERE IT WILL STRIKE
Despite an often intimidating size (bodies up to 6cm and leg spans up to 16cm) tarantulas don't kill people. But their large 1cm long fangs can render painful bites, with severe effects, including nausea, vomiting and fever. They can, however, kill dogs.

DISTRIBUTION
Collectively, the various tarantula species are found across much of mainland Australia.

0

No recorded deaths from Australian tarantulas.

WHITE-TAILED SPIDER

Lampona cylindrata **and** *L. murina*

ALSO KNOWN AS: WHITE-TIPPED SPIDER

Lampona cylindrata **is found in natural and urban areas across southern Australia, from south Queensland to Tasmania and from the east to west coasts.** *L. murina* **is restricted to eastern Australia. Unlike burrowing spiders, white-tailed spiders are vagrant hunters that wander about at night, looking for other spiders to prey upon.**

DISTRIBUTION
Across southern Australia, from QLD to the mid-west coast of WA.

HOW AND WHERE IT WILL STRIKE

These spiders have a reputation for releasing necrotising (flesh-eating) venom, but the scientific evidence doesn't support this. More likely, they have been wrongly blamed for difficult-to-diagnose skin ulcers. Studies show the venom has little effect in people other than mild local pain.

0

No recorded deaths from this spider.

LAND

DID YOU KNOW?
The huge fangs of mouse spiders thrust downwards at a 45-degree angle to help them pierce the tough carapace of the beetles they eat.

MOUSE SPIDER
Missulena spp.

ALSO KNOWN AS: RED-HEADED MOUSE SPIDER

Eight mouse spider species occur across Australia. They're typically found in burrows, often near waterways and are occasionally seen in suburban areas. They tend to be lethargic and are rarely aggressive. Females usually stay in burrows, but males wander around looking for them from late summer to early winter. They are often active by day, unlike their relatives, the funnel-web spiders.

HOW AND WHERE IT WILL STRIKE
Studies have shown funnel-web spider antivenom to be effective for mouse spider envenomation. And because it is sometimes difficult to tell the two species apart, their bites should be treated with the same caution.

DISTRIBUTION
Widespread across the Australian mainland.

0
No deaths have been recorded.

1
A single case of severe envenomation has been recorded.

GARDEN ORB WEAVER SPIDER
Eriophora spp.

ALSO KNOWN AS: AUSTRALIAN ORB WEAVER SPIDER

Garden orb weaver spiders are a typical sight around Australia. They measure between 1.5cm and 3cm and live in many gardens, generally weaving circular webs between trees, on hedges or washing lines, in places where insects are likely to fly and get caught in the sticky threads. Active at night, they hide during the day and rest with their legs withdrawn under the body, hanging off a thread under a leaf or in clothes hanging from washing lines.

HOW AND WHERE IT WILL STRIKE
Web orb weavers wrap their trapped prey in silk before injecting the venom.

DISTRIBUTION
Australia-wide.

!

Their bites have only minor effects, such as localised pain.

DID YOU KNOW?
When food is plentiful, orb weavers will release large prey from their webs to avoid the risk of damaging the silk or being hurt themselves.

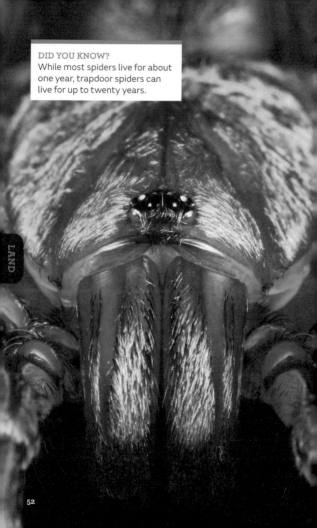

DID YOU KNOW?
While most spiders live for about one year, trapdoor spiders can live for up to twenty years.

TRAPDOOR SPIDER
Family: Idiopidae

ALSO KNOWN AS: ARMOURED TRAPDOOR SPIDER

These spiders are named for the way they camouflage their burrow entrances to trick prey into falling in. They're about 1.5–3cm long and, as is often the case, females are larger than males but males tend to be more aggressive when threatened. As with mouse spiders, trapdoors are often mistaken for funnel-web spiders, especially as the early effects of their bites are similar. These spiders should therefore be treated with extreme caution.

HOW AND WHERE IT WILL STRIKE
Trapdoor spiders cause only minor symptoms in humans, generally inflicting only localised pain, but sometimes nausea, lethargy and malaise can follow.

DISTRIBUTION
Australia-wide.

0
No recorded deaths from trapdoor spider bites.

EUROPEAN HONEY BEE

Apis mellifera

As with European wasps, this 1.5cm honey bee is highly dangerous to people allergic to its venom. Unlike wasps, however, bees leave their stinging barb inserted in their victim, along with a sac of venom and other parts of their abdomen, which ultimately kills the bee. This means that each bee can only sting once.

HOW AND WHERE IT WILL STRIKE

Bees die after stinging, so attack is their last resort. But if a bee feels it or its nest is threatened, it *will* sting, causing pain and localised inflammation. For those people who are allergic, it can potentially produce a deadly anaphylactic reaction.

DISTRIBUTION
Australia-wide.

<3%
of Australians are allergic to bee or wasp venom.

!

On average, allergies to bee venom kill more people than shark attacks.

DID YOU KNOW?
The queen bee makes sure all her
worker bees are doing their jobs
by releasing special chemicals
called pheromones that keep all
the other bees in line.

DID YOU KNOW?
European wasps can be
identified by their bright yellow
and black colours.

EUROPEAN WASP
Vespula germanica

ALSO KNOWN AS: GERMAN WASP,
GERMAN YELLOW-JACKET

European wasps were first found in Australia in 1959 in Tasmania, and by the late 1970s had spread to the mainland. Naturally dormant in European winters, these insects have a particularly long life cycle in Australia due to our relatively warmer temperatures. Nesting underground and inside the walls of houses, they can establish colonies of up to 100,000 individuals.

HOW AND WHERE IT WILL STRIKE

These wasps pack a painful sting. Because their stingers aren't barbed as they are in bees, they don't rip out and kill the host, therefore they can sting repeatedly, which they do if annoyed.

DISTRIBUTION
South-eastern and south-western Australia and Tasmania.

!
The sting is not deadly unless the recipient is allergic to wasp venom. In such cases, seek immediate medical attention because fatalities are possible.

BULL ANT
Myrmecia spp.

ALSO KNOWN AS: BULLDOG ANTS

Bull ants, which can reach 2.5cm in length, belong to the almost exclusively Australian ant genus *Myrmecia*. Bull ants are more dangerous than other biting ants, not because of the toxicity of their venom, but because of their aggression and how frequently they come into contact with people. About 1 per cent of humans are allergic to ant venom.

HOW AND WHERE IT WILL STRIKE
A bull ant will clamp onto its target with large, pincer-like jaws, then repeatedly inject venom with the stinger on its abdomen. The venom is painful but not life-threatening, except to those allergic to it, who will require immediate medical attention.

DISTRIBUTION
Australia-wide.

0
No recorded deaths, although severe anaphylactic shock has occurred.

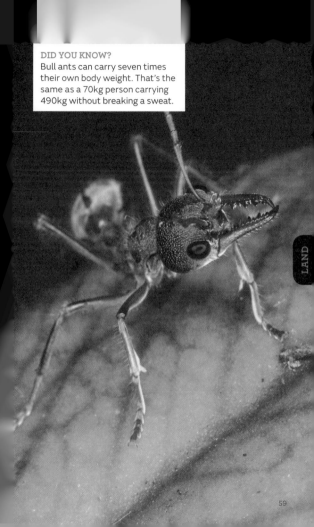

DID YOU KNOW?
Bull ants can carry seven times their own body weight. That's the same as a 70kg person carrying 490kg without breaking a sweat.

DID YOU KNOW?
These ticks have also been
blamed for the spread of
Flinders Island spotted fever.

PARALYSIS TICK
Ixodes holocyclus

ALSO KNOWN AS: AUSTRALIAN PARALYSIS TICK

Marsupials, particularly bandicoots, are the usual hosts of this native Australian creature. They have developed immunity to tick toxin, but introduced animals haven't and neither have humans. Tick eggs hatch into six-legged larvae which moult into eight-legged nymphs, then adults. After each moult they drop off their old host and reattach themselves to a new one.

HOW AND WHERE IT WILL STRIKE
Female ticks are capable of causing fatal paralysis in dogs and other domestic animals, and more rarely in young children and the elderly. Symptoms of tick toxin in humans include flu-like symptoms, dizziness, limb weakness, facial paralysis and anaphylactic shock.

DISTRIBUTION
Coastal regions of eastern Australia.

0

No recorded human deaths, although many cases of paralysis have been recorded and many deaths in domestic animals.

CENTIPEDE
Class: *Chilopoda*

Fast, agile and a little bit creepy, Australian centipedes are known for packing a powerful punch. Unlike millipedes, centipedes have just one pair of limbs per body segment, a pair of fangs under the head and a pair of antennae. The giant centipede, found throughough Australia, can grow to 14cm long, and has either 25 or 27 body segments with 21 or 23 pairs of legs.

HOW AND WHERE IT WILL STRIKE
Centipedes use their abbreviated arms, called forcipules, to inject small amounts of highly toxic venom into their prey. The stings can be painful for up to a week.

DISTRIBUTION
Leaf litter of rainforests and woodlands or under rocks in the desert.

0
No deaths in Australia. Some species of centipede overseas have caused renal failure and been fatal to children and the elderly.

LAND

DID YOU KNOW?
Female forest scorpions give birth to live young, which they carry on their backs until old enough to fend for themselves.

FOREST SCORPION
Cercophonius squama

ALSO KNOWN AS: WOOD SCORPION

The forest scorpion likes to live hidden among leaf litter where it can hunt small insects. This arachnid, that can vary between creamy yellow and dark brown, grows up to 40mm and can live for as long as three years.

HOW AND WHERE IT WILL STRIKE
When disturbed, the forest scorpion will arch its tail high over its back. If the threat doesn't back off, it will then whip its stinger down and into whatever is threatening it, including people.

DISTRIBUTION
South-western Western Australia, and south-eastern Australia.

0

No recorded deaths although the sting can lead to intense pain, swelling and sometimes anaphylactic shock.

SOUTHERN CASSOWARY

Casuarius casuarius

ALSO KNOWN AS: DOUBLE-WATTLED CASSOWARY,
TWO-WATTLED CASSOWARY,
AUSTRALIAN CASSOWARY

This large, flightless tropical bird can reach 175cm in height. It has stiff, bristly black plumage with a distinctive blue face and neck, which is also red on the nape and it has two red wattles hanging down around the throat. A horn-like casque sits atop the head.

HOW AND WHERE IT WILL STRIKE

The southern cassowary is often heard long before it's seen. Its rumbling calls are usually produced in response to potential danger. When threatened it will use its powerful legs, which are armed with elongated sharp claws, to strike at an opponent.

DISTRIBUTION

Tropical rainforests of northern Queensland.

1
Death

!

Numerous recorded attacks including serious woundings.

DID YOU KNOW?
The southern cassowary forages on
the forest floor for fallen fruit and
is capable of safely digesting some
fruits that are toxic to other animals.

LAND

PLATYPUS
Ornithorhynchus anatinus

This ever-mysterious monotreme is armed with a dangerous stinging apparatus. However, it only occurs in the male of the species. A spur located above each of its back feet secretes a venom, the production of which increases during the breeding season – which is when they're most likely to use it.

HOW AND WHERE IT WILL STRIKE
The spur is most commonly used in fights with other males. Tests show that the venom contains enzymes that cause severe pain, paralysis and respiratory failure.

DISTRIBUTION
Eastern Queensland; eastern NSW; eastern, south-eastern and central Victoria; and Tasmania.

!
Human injuries have been recorded, and, while not fatal, have caused pain and permanent damage.

GIDEE-GIDEE
Abrus precatorius

ALSO KNOWN AS: CRAB'S EYES,
JEQUIRITY BEAN, ROSARY PEA,
PRECATORY BEAN, INDIAN LIQUORICE

This delicate looking plant is very pretty, with pink or purple and white flowers and bright red and black berries. However, this plant is extremely poisonous. Just touching the beans can lead to rashes and skin irritation, but eating them can be fatal.

HOW AND WHERE IT WILL STRIKE
Seeds are extremely toxic and if chewed can kill an adult in just minutes or slowly over 1–3 days, depending on the amount ingested. The poison in one seed is enough to kill a human, but if the seed is not crushed in any way it can pass through the body without causing harm.

DISTRIBUTION
Northern WA, Queensland and the NT.

?

There have been a number of reported deaths, mainly of children, but no official estimate of how many people have died from eating this plant.

DID YOU KNOW?
Gidee-gidee beans
contain ricin, a potent
toxin that scientists have
been trying to weaponise
since World War I.

DID YOU KNOW?
Although introduced animal species as well as humans are affected by this plant, many native species aren't and happily climb in and even eat it.

GYMPIE-GYMPIE
Dendrocnide moroides

ALSO KNOWN AS: SHINING STINGING LEAF TREE,
STINGING BUSH, MULBERRY-LEAVED STINGER,
SUICIDE PLANT, GYMPIE STINGER, MOONLIGHTER

Just brushing up against a gympie-gympie can be excruciatingly painful, so give these trees a wide berth. Even standing next to one without a face mask can cause painful sneezing and nose bleeds, because the poisonous hairs that float around the tree can drift into your nose.

HOW AND WHERE IT WILL STRIKE
When the plant is touched, tiny silicon hairs break off and penetrate your skin. The hairs deliver a neurotoxin that causes extreme pain, swelling and blistering. The only way to get relief from this pain is to use a wax strip to remove the hairs. If all the hairs are not removed the pain can last for months.

DISTRIBUTION
North from northern coastal NSW, but most prolific in southern Queensland and Cape York.

0
No proven human fatalities but there are stories of people committing suicide because of the pain.

MILKY MANGROVE
Excoecaria agallocha

ALSO KNOWN AS: BLIND-YOUR-EYE MANGROVE,
RIVER POISON TREE, BLINDING TREE

Milky mangroves may grow as shrubs or trees up to 15m in height, and occur at the tidal limits. The bark is grey to brown in colour; the timber is light, soft and pale, and is used overseas for incense and in canoe construction. The sap is used for fish poison and medicinally in the treatment of chronic ulcerous diseases such as leprosy.

DISTRIBUTION
From northern coastal NSW, through QLD and NT to WA.

HOW AND WHERE IT WILL STRIKE
The major feature of this mangrove is the milky sap that seeps from the plant when branches or leaves are broken. The sap is poisonous and can cause severe skin irritation and temporary blindness if contact is made with the eyes.

0
No deaths recorded; however, the milky exudate can cause intense pain and blistering that can last days.

DID YOU KNOW?
Even dried and powdered leaves contain the poison that can kill fish very quickly.

SEA

Saltwater crocodile
Crocodylus porosus

DID YOU KNOW?
The longest croc
ever measured and
verified was 6.4m
(21ft). It could
have weighed
more than 1000kg.
In Australia, there
are unverified
reports of crocs
up to 8m.

SALTWATER CROCODILE
Crocodylus porosus

ALSO KNOWN AS: SALTIE, ESTUARINE CROCODILE, INDO-PACIFIC CROCODILE

Salties are found mostly in coastal river systems, estuaries, some offshore islands and occasionally a long way upstream in freshwater rivers, hundreds of kilometres from salt water. Protected since 1974, populations have recovered almost back to pre-colonial numbers and they require careful management around populated areas.

HOW AND WHERE IT WILL STRIKE

If you enter the water or even stray too near the water's edge in crocodile territory, the risk of attack is extremely high. Heed all warning signs and, if you are unsure, err on the side of caution when travelling in Australia's tropics.

DISTRIBUTION
Northern Australia.

1-2
Known deaths per year.

4-10
Non-fatal attacks per year.

FRESHWATER CROCODILE

Crocodylus johnstoni

ALSO KNOWN AS: FRESHIE, FISH CROCODILE,
JOHNSTONE'S RIVER CROCODILE,
JOHNSTONE'S CROCODILE

Smaller and less aggressive than their saltwater relatives, freshies reach an average length of 2m and are distinguished by a more slender snout. They inhabit freshwater and brackish rivers and lakes in northern Australia. If approached or threatened they will inflate and shudder their bodies, causing surrounding water to ripple violently, while gaping and emitting a low-pitched warning growl.

HOW AND WHERE IT WILL STRIKE

Freshies are shy and will avoid contact with humans, but they have been known to bite if they mistake an arm or leg under water for a tasty fish. Their sharp dagger-like teeth can inflict severe lacerations.

DISTRIBUTION

Water bodies in northern Australia.

0

No recorded deaths, although a bite can cause permanent damage and can cause the loss of limbs.

DID YOU KNOW?
Freshwater crocodiles can perform a 'high walk' to move overland, whereby the body is held high so that the belly and most of the tail are not touching the ground.

SEA

DID YOU KNOW?
It is thought that females don't reach maturity until aged 12–18 years. For males it's 8–10 years.

GREAT WHITE SHARK
Carcharodon carcharias

ALSO KNOWN AS: WHITE SHARK, WHITE POINTER

Great whites are apex predators of the ocean, capable of growing to 7m long. They are naturally curious and investigate things by biting them. It's thought that many attacks on humans are these sorts of exploratory bites. Great white numbers have dropped significantly in the past 50 years and they are now protected in Australian waters.

HOW AND WHERE IT WILL STRIKE
Great whites may attack surfers on boards, because they look like seals from below. When hunting, they dive down and then swim upwards fast to deliver a quick, stunning blow. But, if curious, they may swim from behind and bite quickly before retreating slightly.

DISTRIBUTION
Australia's southern coast.

46% of shark attacks in Australia in 2016 were attributed to great white sharks.

OCEANIC WHITETIP SHARK
Carcharhinus longimanus

ALSO KNOWN AS: BROWN SHARK, NIGANO SHARK,
SILVERTIP SHARK, BROWN MILBERT'S SANDBAR SHARK,
OCEANIC WHITE-TIPPED WHALER

Oceanic whitetips are stocky sharks with distinctive rounded tips on their dorsal and pectoral fins. These fin tips feature white markings, as does the lower caudal, or tail, fin. These features make the sharks easy to identify. They vary in overall colour from dark to light grey to dull brown, sometimes with a bronze or blue tinge.

DISTRIBUTION
Around the east and west coasts in tropical to temperate waters.

HOW AND WHERE IT WILL STRIKE
Being open-ocean dwellers, oceanic whitetips respond quickly to the rare appearance of any potential food. As predators they are very bold, aggressive and seem to lack the inherent caution shown by most other shark species.

?

The number of attacks is unknown, but this species is believed to be responsible for hundreds of deaths, the vast majority occurring after air and sea disasters.

DID YOU KNOW?
They are known to form loose groups
when a food source is found, such as
a whale carcass, and are often seen
following tropical toothed whales,
such as short-finned pilot whales.

DID YOU KNOW?
Female bull sharks have a gestation period of 10–11 months and give birth to live young.

BULL SHARK
Carcharhinus leucas

**ALSO KNOWN AS: ZAMBEZI SHARK,
NICARAGUA SHARK, GANGES RIVER SHARK,
RIVER SHARK, FRESHWATER WHALER,
ESTUARY WHALER, CUB SHARK,
SWAN RIVER WHALER**

This hefty shark can grow up to 3.4m long and gets its common name from its huge size and great strength. Bull sharks will eat anything they find in the water, from fish to rats, and can live in fresh water. This means they often come in contact with humans in rivers and along the coast.

HOW AND WHERE IT WILL STRIKE
These sharks travel up freshwater rivers and hang around the coast, hunting for anything that moves. They will swim in quickly and chomp down with their large, powerful jaws, which can amputate limbs and cause death.

DISTRIBUTION
From south-western WA, along the northern coast and down to the central coast of New South Wales.

1 of 4
shark species responsible for the most attacks on people.

TIGER SHARK
Galeocerdo cuvier

ALSO KNOWN AS: SPOTTED SHARK,
MANEATER SHARK

This shark's common name comes from the dark stripes that cover its back. These are particularly clear on the young pups and may help them hide from predators. Voracious hunters that also have a reputation as scavengers, these sharks often come in contact with humans. They can grow to 4m long and weigh 600kg.

HOW AND WHERE IT WILL STRIKE

Tigers are among the shark species most dangerous to people. After great whites and bull sharks, they are responsible for the highest number of attacks. But they don't target people; they are indiscriminate hunters that will try anything that moves.

DISTRIBUTION
All along the top of Australia from Shark Bay, WA, to the northern coast of QLD.

100
Estimated attacks in Australian waters, where a tiger shark is believed to have been the culprit.

DID YOU KNOW?
Tiger sharks will eat absolutely anything and this has earned them the nickname 'wastebaskets of the sea'. Some adult sharks have been found with tyres and licence plates in their stomachs.

SEA

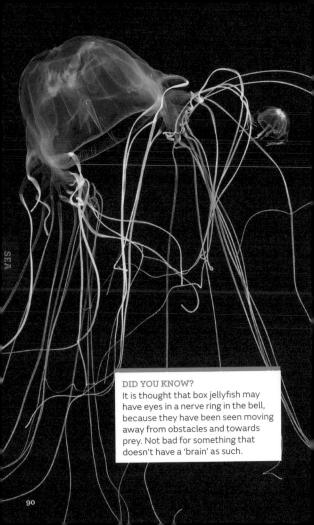

DID YOU KNOW?
It is thought that box jellyfish may have eyes in a nerve ring in the bell, because they have been seen moving away from obstacles and towards prey. Not bad for something that doesn't have a 'brain' as such.

BOX JELLYFISH
Chironex fleckeri

ALSO KNOWN AS: SEA WASP, INDRINGA, SEA STINGER

Known for lurking in the warm seas along the northern coast of Australia, the box jellyfish is one of the most potent stingers in the world. This translucent marine creature is most prevalent during summer months, with all recorded deaths between October and May.

HOW AND WHERE IT WILL STRIKE
Venom is injected via small stinging cells called nematocysts along the tentacles, and the severity of the sting correlates with the amount of tentacle that touches the skin. Stings are excruciating and the venom attacks the muscles around the lungs and heart. Paralysis of both these organs is the main cause of death in untreated cases.

DISTRIBUTION
Northern Queensland, NT and WA.

70
Estimated deaths.

3m
tentacles wrap around the unsuspecting prey.

IRUKANDJI JELLYFISH
Families: Alatinidae, Carukiidae, Tamoyidae

ALSO KNOWN AS: IRUKANDJI BOX JELLYFISH, SEA WASP

Irukandji is the collective name given to a range of box jellyfish species that have just one tentacle arising in each lower corner of the bell. They can cause 'Irukandji syndrome', and, depending on which species is responsible, symptoms may vary and be severe and life-threatening. Although Irukandji are often found in deep water, swarms can form at the surface near swimming beaches.

HOW AND WHERE IT WILL STRIKE
The syndrome can develop 30 minutes after a sting with a sequence of symptoms from lower back pain, profuse sweating and vomiting, to headaches, nausea, anxiety and high blood pressure.

DISTRIBUTION
Tropical waters of northern Australia.

Alatina alata shown

2
Recorded deaths since 1883.

50-100
People on average are sent to hospital annually from being stung by Irukandji.

DID YOU KNOW?
Research is underway to develop an antivenom for irukandji stings and it is likely that we will have a useable antivenom in the very near future.

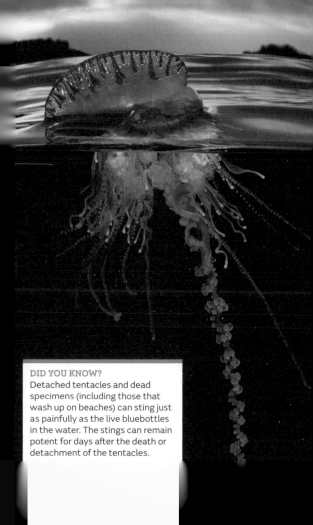

DID YOU KNOW?
Detached tentacles and dead specimens (including those that wash up on beaches) can sting just as painfully as the live bluebottles in the water. The stings can remain potent for days after the death or detachment of the tentacles.

BLUEBOTTLE
Physalia physalis

ALSO KNOWN AS: PORTUGUESE MAN-OF-WAR

Known as bluebottles because of the indigo floats that carry them across the oceans, they are some of Australia's peskiest stingers. Each bluebottle is a colony of individual 'zooids' that can't live separately and have allocated tasks for their collective survival. Their trailing tentacles are typically 10m long but can be up to 30m and they carry the stings.

HOW AND WHERE IT WILL STRIKE

The tentacles contain venom-filled nematocysts (stinging cells) for killing small prey. Although painful, the venom isn't fatal in humans, but some people can have a life-threatening allergic reaction. Stings can cause severe pain, leaving whip-like, red welts on the skin for days.

DISTRIBUTION

Throughout the world in warmer seas; habitat generally encircles Australia and extends south as far as Tasmania.

10,000
Estimated number of people stung each summer.

0
No recorded fatalities in Australia.

Blue-ringed octopus
Hapalochlaena sp.

BLUE-RINGED OCTOPUS
Hapalochlaena spp.

ALSO KNOWN AS: BLUE-LINED OCTOPUS

These tiny cephalopods may be seen hunting in rock pools near Australian beaches. Despite their small size, they are the the world's most deadly octopus. They're shy creatures that would prefer to avoid confrontation and their blue rings will pulse a warning to stay away. Unfortunately, this can have the opposite effect on children who are often drawn to the bright display.

HOW AND WHERE IT WILL STRIKE

The bite is virtually painless and often goes unnoticed, but within just 10 minutes a victim can be fighting for life. Neurotoxins can cause vomiting, breathing difficulties, heart failure, paralysis and blindness.

DISTRIBUTION
Entire Australian coastline in warm, shallow waters.

3
Estimated deaths. There have been no deaths since the 1960s, however, and hospital admissions are uncommon.

DID YOU KNOW?
A blue-ringed octopus has blue blood,
three hearts and enough poison to kill
26 humans. The same nerve toxins
injected by a blue-ring are found
in parts of fugu fish – a pricey but
dangerous Japanese delicacy.

DID YOU KNOW?
Cone snail venom is the source of a drug called Ziconotide, used to relieve chronic pain.

SEA

CONE SNAIL
Conus spp.

ALSO KNOWN AS: CONE SHELL

Creeping along the bottom of the ocean are venomous, predatory gastropods, commonly known as cone snails. They hunt by extending a harpoon-like proboscis that fires when prey, such as fish, come close enough. The venom needs to be powerful to instantly stop fish from swimming away from these slow-moving creatures.

HOW AND WHERE IT WILL STRIKE
Humans are mainly stung when they pick up these shells, because they will also use their venom for defence. The shells can be large and beautifully marked, making them popular with collectors.

1
Death recorded in Australia, in 1935.

15
Healthy adults could be killed from a single sting.

ESTUARINE STONEFISH
Synanceia horrida

ALSO KNOWN AS: HORRID STONEFISH, ROUGH STONEFISH, TRUE STONEFISH

One of two species of stonefish found in Australian waters, this warty brown fish is one of the most venomous in the world. Stonefish carry lethal venom because they can't swim away from danger easily. Their stubby fins make them poor swimmers and they can be seen using the fins to crawl along the sea floor like a crab.

DISTRIBUTION
Northern Australia, from Shark Bay, WA, to Tweed River, NSW.

HOW AND WHERE IT WILL STRIKE
When threatened the fish erects its 13 dorsal spines and injects its venom into the skin of the attacker. For humans, envenomation with stonefish toxins can lead to paralysis, tissue necrosis, difficulty breathing, pain, and (in extreme cases) heart failure and death.

0

No cases of death, although there have been many serious envenomations.

DID YOU KNOW?
Stonefish have the ability to survive out of water for up to 24 hours. This is particularly useful for a coastal-living fish that can become beached between tides.

DID YOU KNOW?
The reef stonefish is the most venomous fish in the world.

REEF STONEFISH
Synanceia verrucosa

Reef stonefish are superbly camouflaged and can easily be mistaken for coral. They have 30 dorsal fin spines that carry an extremely toxic venom. They can be distinguished from their close relative, the estuarine stonefish, by the deep indentation between the eyes. An antivenom was developed in 1959.

DISTRIBUTION
From Brisbane
to Broome.

No reported deaths in Australia, but stonefish stings are potentially fatal.

HOW AND WHERE IT WILL STRIKE

These fish can survive for hours in small pools when the tide goes out and are encountered most commonly when trodden on by unsuspecting people wading in shallow water. The severity of the venom is relative to the number of punctures made by the spines.

COMMON LIONFISH
Pterois volitans

ALSO KNOWN AS: BUTTERFLY COD, FEATHERFINS, FIREFISH, LIONFISH, RED FIREFISH, SCORPION COD, TURKEYFISH, ZEBRAFISH

The lionfish may get one of its common names from its bright red and yellow stripes or from its many large, mane-like fins. But, unlike the lion of the cat family, it's not the teeth you have to worry about here, but the sharp, venomous spines hidden in the fins of this highly distinctive creature.

HOW AND WHERE IT WILL STRIKE

The lionfish will make no effort to swim away if threatened. Instead, contact with any of its dorsal, anal or pelvic fin spines can result in the injection of venom. Effects of the venom include extreme pain, breathing difficulties, vomiting, fever, dizziness and sweating.

DISTRIBUTION
South-western WA, all along the northern tropical coast and along the southern coast of NSW.

0

No reported deaths but the pain is intense and some people can suffer anaphylactic reactions.

DID YOU KNOW?
Dead or alive, lionfish spines can still sting, so give these fish a wide berth.

DID YOU KNOW?
Toadfish inflate their stomachs with water when threatened, but, when caught by fishermen, have to use air instead. They struggle to get the air out again and may not be able to deflate themselves if they're put back in the water.

SEA

SMOOTH TOADFISH
Tetractenos glaber

ALSO KNOWN AS: TOADO FISH,
'TOADIE', BLOWFISH

The smooth toadfish is a member of the puffer fish family and it too can inflate itself, although not as impressively as true puffers. The toxins in this fish have no antidote, but the fish is only dangerous if eaten. So don't make a meal out of toadfish and you should be fine.

HOW AND WHERE IT WILL STRIKE

The toadfish is harmless unless it is actually eaten. When threatened, the toadfish will inflate like a puffer fish in order to scare off predators.

DISTRIBUTION
Common along Australia's eastern coastline, from southern Queensland to Tasmania and SA.

?

Several deaths are thought to have occurred as a result of eating toadfish flesh.

STINGRAY
Families: Dasyatidae, Gymnuridae,
Myliobatidae and Urolophidae

Stingrays are generally docile; however, many come armed with rarely used but potentially dangerous bony spines at the end of their tails. They swim along ocean floors, feeding on small crustaceans and other invertebrates. They'll often lie on the bottom, partially covered with sand, and this is often when people stand on them and receive a painful jab to the foot.

HOW AND WHERE IT WILL STRIKE
When stepped on or threatened, or if their vertebral column is touched, stingrays tend to thrust their spine into the perceived attacker. This spine releases painful venom and can cause deep lacerations that can result in infection from bacteria.

DISTRIBUTION
All through Australian waters, but most often in southern QLD and central WA.

!
There have been few deaths from stingrays. Although Steve Irwin's death in 2006 from stingray jabs highlighted the risk they pose.

DID YOU KNOW?
Stingrays are cartilaginous fish. Like their close relatives the sharks, they don't have bones. Instead they have skeletons made of cartilage.

SEA

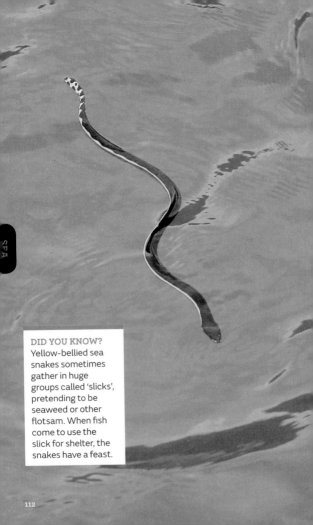

DID YOU KNOW?
Yellow-bellied sea
snakes sometimes
gather in huge
groups called 'slicks',
pretending to be
seaweed or other
flotsam. When fish
come to use the
slick for shelter, the
snakes have a feast.

YELLOW-BELLIED SEA SNAKE
Pelamis platurus

ALSO KNOWN AS: PELAGIC SNAKE

These snakes move quickly and gracefully through the sea, but are completely helpless on land. Unlike land snakes, whose scales help them grip the ground to move, sea snakes have smooth skin, which means they can't move over ground the same way. These snakes can also breathe through their skin, which helps them stay under water for long periods of time.

DISTRIBUTION
Found in most Australian waters with the exception of the colder southern coastline.

HOW AND WHERE IT WILL STRIKE
Their paddle-shaped tail, yellow underbelly and black back makes them easy to spot. This 'countershading' helps them hunt as they float on the ocean's surface. Their colouring disguises them from prey swimming below and potential predators above.

0

No recorded deaths from yellow-bellied sea snakes.

BEAKED SEA SNAKE
Enhydrina zweifeli

ALSO KNOWN AS: COMMON SEA SNAKE,
HOOK-NOSED SEA SNAKE,
VALAKADYN SEA SNAKE

Like other sea snakes, this one is highly adapted to sea life, with a paddle-like tail for swimming and valved nostrils that close under water. It grows to 1.4m long, and is a dull olive-green or greenish-grey with a whitish belly and dark cross-bands. Sea snakes are among the world's most venomous snakes – this species is one of the most dangerous and more aggressive than most. Fortunately, they rarely bite.

HOW AND WHERE IT WILL STRIKE
Most fatalities from beaked sea snake bites occur where it frequently comes into contact with humans, such as in shallow estuaries or when it is removed from fishing nets.

DISTRIBUTION
Found in the tropics between Darwin, NT, and Rockhampton, in QLD.

50%
of all sea snake bites are caused by this species, but exact numbers are not known due to remote distribution and limited records.

DID YOU KNOW?
Beaked sea snakes in Australia have recently been named as a distinct species, long confused with similar snakes in Asia.

INDEX AND CREDITS

Eastern brown snake
Pseudonaja textilis

*Killer OZ: A collection of the 50 most deadly
and dangerous Australian animals and plants*

First published in 2017
Australian Geographic, an imprint of
Bauer Media Ltd, 54 Park Street, Sydney NSW 2000
Telephone: 02 9263 9813
Email: editorial@ausgeo.com.au
www.australiangeographic.com.au
© Australian Geographic and Bauer Media
All rights reserved.

National Library of Australia Cataloguing-in-Publication entry
Title: *Killer OZ: A collection of the 50 most deadly
and dangerous Australian animals and plants*
ISBN 978 1 7424 5858 8 (hardback)
Dewey Number: 591.650994

Australian Geographic Editor-in-Chief: Chrissie Goldrick
Designer: Filip Bartkowiak and Mike Rossi
Text: Madeleine van der Linden and Jess Teideman
Proofreader: Sue McCreery
Production Editor and image management: Jess Teideman
Print production: Christopher Clear

Chief Executive Officer, Bauer Media Group: Nick Chan
Publishing Director, Bauer Media Specialist Division: Cornelia Schulze
Publisher, Bauer Media Specialist Division: Jo Runciman

Printed in China by Leo Paper Products Ltd.